THE TWENTY MIRACLES
OF SAINT NICOLAS

Who was born in the
third century of our
era, and died in the
year three-hundred
and forty-five, leaving
behind him many songs
and legends of his won-
derful powers.

BERNARDA BRYSON

with illustrations by the author

An Atlantic Monthly Press Book
Little, Brown and Company
Boston • Toronto

ATLANTIC–LITTLE, BROWN BOOKS
ARE PUBLISHED BY
LITTLE, BROWN AND COMPANY
IN ASSOCIATION WITH
THE ATLANTIC MONTHLY PRESS

Published simultaneously in Canada
by Little, Brown & Company (Canada) Limited

PRINTED IN THE UNITED STATES OF AMERICA

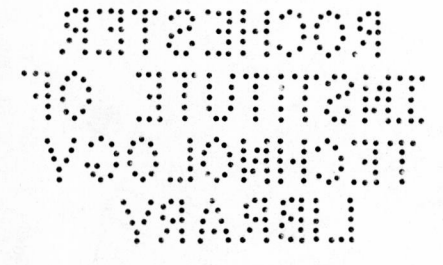

For Susanna

Saint Nicolas keeps the mariners
from daunger and diseas
That beaten are with boystrous waves
and tost in dreadfull seas.

—*Barnaby Goodge*

Contents

ere is the story of Saint Nicolas, Bishop of Myra, patron saint of mariners, moneylenders, thieves and children; protector of travelers, turners, dyers, coopers, boatmen, bootmakers, sawyers, seedmen, mercers, merchants, Greeks, cities, Jews, packers, spinsters, pirates, Russians, pickpockets, haberdashers, children, fishermen, pilgrims, prisoners, parish clerks, sailors and unwedded maids; defender of the Faith and maker of many true miracles.

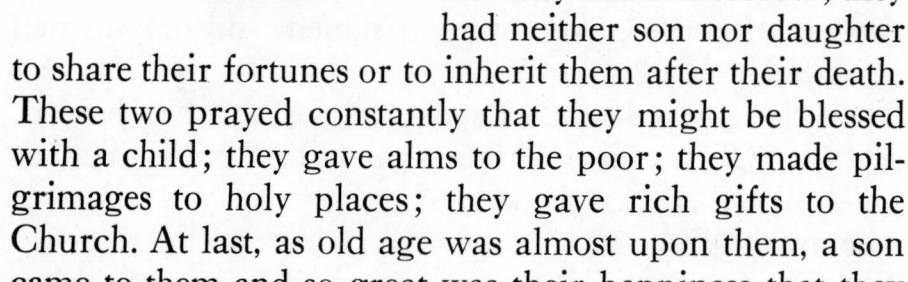

THE BIRTH OF SAINT NICOLAS

Seventeen hundred years ago, more or less, there lived in Patara, in the country of Lycia, a good merchant and his true and pious wife. These two were blessed with great wealth and with almost every good thing the heart could wish for. But they had one sorrow; they had neither son nor daughter to share their fortunes or to inherit them after their death. These two prayed constantly that they might be blessed with a child; they gave alms to the poor; they made pilgrimages to holy places; they gave rich gifts to the Church. At last, as old age was almost upon them, a son came to them and so great was their happiness that they named him Nicolas, which means "victorious."

On the day of the child's birth there was great rejoicing in this household. But such happiness was short-lived and soon turned to sorrow. For the nurses who had taken the baby away to bathe him returned, running in terror.

The first said, "The child is bewitched." The second said,

3

"He is possessed by the Devil." The third said, "Although he is but an hour old, he stood erect in his tub and spoke to us in a strange tongue." And the fourth said, "He spoke to us in Greek, which is the language of pagans."

Then the women went away and swore that they would never again lay hands upon the child.

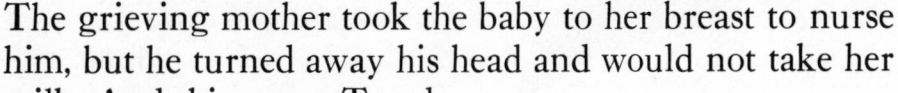

The grieving mother took the baby to her breast to nurse him, but he turned away his head and would not take her milk. And this was a Tuesday.

On the following day the child nursed and laughed and was happy as any normal child. And that was Wednesday. And again on Thursday the child took milk. But on Friday he refused to take any nourishment and only turned away his head.

Then the grieved mother spoke, almost as if to herself, saying, "Oh my dear child, what is this curse that has fallen upon us? Am I made of poison that you refuse to take my milk?"

To her great surprise the baby replied to her, speaking clearly, "Oh Mother," he said, "do you not know that today is Friday and is a fasting day, and that Tuesdays are fasting days also, when the good and pious take no food?"

Then the mother was full of joy, for she saw that her child would grow up to be a holy man, perhaps even a Saint, and that he was in no way possessed by the Devil.

"But tell me, dear child," she then asked, "why it was that you spoke to the women in Greek, which is the language of pagans."

"Because," replied the child, "the Greeks will be brought into the Church and Greek will become the language of the Bible."

So it was that at the very beginning of his life Saint Nicolas had made two miracles, the miracle of standing and speaking, and the miracle of observing the fast.

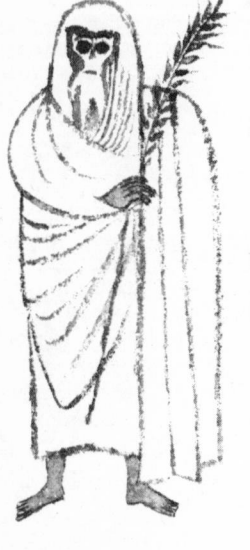

THE BOY BISHOP

hen Saint Nicolas was nine years of age, a killing plague fell upon the country of Lycia. Hundreds of people died in this plague and among them were his father and mother. The boy Nicolas had no wish to remain alone in his parents' house, so he sold it. He then divided all his wealth among the poor, and joining a company of traveling merchants he set out on foot to see the world.

It happened that not far away, in the city of Myra, a great bishop had also died in the plague. All the bishops from that part of the world, as well as an old and noble patriarch, had come together to elect a new Bishop of Myra. On the night before the new bishop was to be chosen, the patriarch had a dream in which he was visited by an angel. The angel said, "Let that one who is named Nicolas be elected Bishop of Myra."

On the following day when all the holy men had gathered inside the church, the old man told of his dream. Then he said, "Let that one who is named Nicolas come forward." But no one moved, for there was not one among them that had that name.

6

The churchmen sat looking at each other, waiting and wondering what could be the meaning of the dream, when the doors of the building opened and a young boy came inside, and, as a very old book says, "He stood before them simple as a dove."

"Who are you?" a deacon cried out. "And how do you, a young boy, dare to walk inside the church when the holy fathers are in council?"

"My name is Nicolas," said the boy. "I have come here because I have no other home."

The fathers sat looking at each other in great doubt and awe, for they saw that this was indeed a miracle. Then they elected Nicolas to be Bishop of Myra and called him "Venerable Brother" though he was but nine years of age. Saint Nicolas now made a vow that he would forever serve the Church and that he would bring the New Faith to the pagans and the heathens and the idol worshipers, that he would seek to vanquish the Devil, who was in those days abroad in the world, and that he would himself always be the protector of the poor and the helpless. And all these things he did and was.

HOW SAINT NICOLAS BECAME THE
PATRON OF CHILDREN

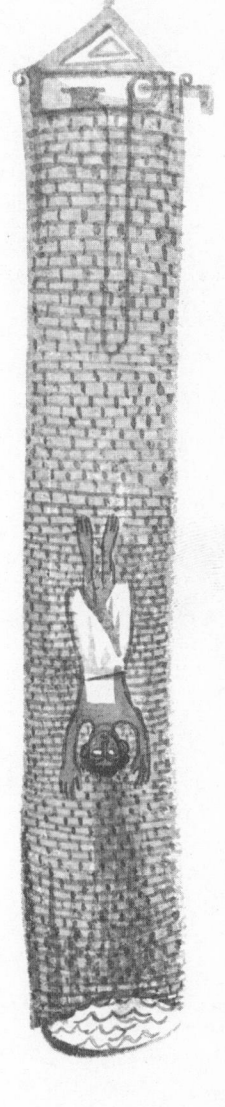

The people of the city of Myra were most surprised that a small boy had been elected to the great office of bishop. For it would be his duty to tell them what was wrong and what was right, and how can a small boy know such things?

Many doubted that he could.

One day there was a church procession in which the people of the town walked together carrying many-colored banners, playing upon horns and bagpipes and singing songs, all to celebrate the election of the new Boy Bishop. Saint Nicolas walked with them under a canopy that had gold fringe and tassels of gold and brightly painted posts.

Now the Devil seeing this procession, and seeing how the sickness and sorrows of the people were turned to joy, was filled with envy and rage and decided to take vengeance upon the town.

There was, among the people, a small boy who in order to see better had climbed upon the brink of a well. "Just right!" said the Devil to himself, and he pushed the boy into the well.

9

But Saint Nicolas, who was at that moment passing by, heard the boy's cries and he instantly raised his right hand and made a certain sign, so that the boy was lifted by miracle out of the well, and was set by unseen hands safe upon the ground.

Thus all the people came to know that he would be a good, wise and powerful bishop, perhaps even a saint. They praised and thanked him with many songs, and after that time he came to be known as the patron saint of children. But the Devil vowed that he would come again, and that he would still have his vengeance on the people and on Saint Nicolas.

THE MIRACLE OF THE THREE
DOWERLESS MAIDENS

ld men of the city tell of a nobleman who had once been rich but was now poor. He had little left in this world except three beautiful daughters, and of these the oldest was of an age to be married. But before she could be married it was necessary that the father offer a dowry of gold to whatever young man wanted to be her husband. The more gold he could offer, the better would be the husband whom she could marry. But this poor nobleman had no gold at all.

Being altogether weary of his poverty, he decided to sacrifice his oldest daughter by selling her into slavery and a life of shame. Thus he calculated that he would have enough money to furnish a dowry for his second daughter, and to keep himself in comfort.

So he bargained with an evil old woman who promised to give him a handsome sum of money when he delivered the girl into her hands.

On a certain night he spoke to his daughter, saying, "Make yourself ready, my dearest girl, for tomorrow we will go on a long journey and see many wonderful things." The daughter was very pleased at this news. She thanked her father, put together her few possessions and went happily to bed.

11

But no sooner had she fallen asleep than she seemed to hear a voice whispering in her ear. The voice spoke as follows: "My dear girl," it said, "your father has no intention of taking you upon a long journey. Instead he intends to sell you into slavery and to use the money as a dowry for your sister. In the morning you will find a round bag of gold inside your stocking. You must take this gold for your dowry and demand of your father that he get you a husband."

In the morning the poor girl wakened shivering: "What a terrible nightmare I have had," she thought. "How glad I am that it was only a dream!"

But, when she was about to draw on her stocking, she found in it a round bag of gold, and then she knew that the dream must be true.

So she went to her father and told him that at last she had money for a dowry and that he must secure a husband for her. The nobleman had no choice but to do as she asked. So he found her a husband; she was wed and went far away.

And the nobleman was as poor as ever.

Soon his second daughter came of age and he decided that he would again try his plan. At least he would have enough money for his third daughter and himself.

Again he bargained with the evil woman, and again she promised she would give him a handsome sum when he delivered his second daughter into her hands.

Then he spoke to his second daughter, saying, "Make yourself ready, my dearest girl, for tomorrow we will go on a long journey and see many wonderful things."

The daughter was very happy indeed, and she thanked her father and put together her few possessions and went to bed.

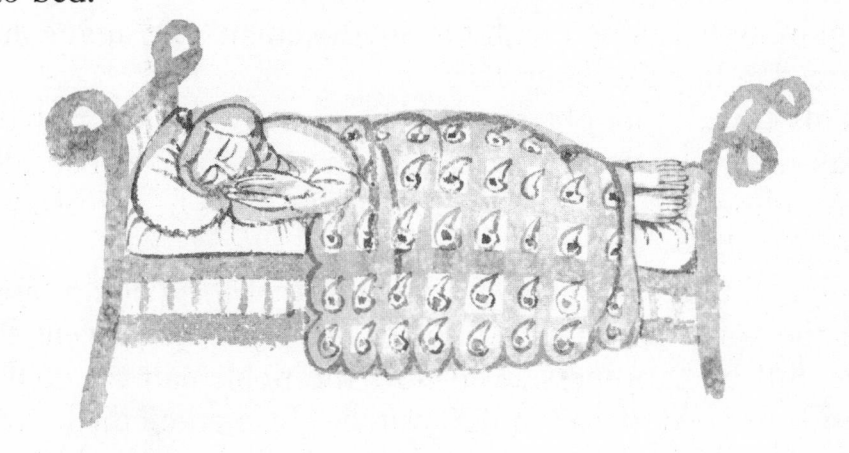

No sooner had she fallen asleep than she too heard the voice, which said, "My dear girl, your father has no intention of taking you upon a long journey. Instead he intends to sell you into slavery and to use the money as a dowry for your sister. In the morning you will find a round bag of gold inside your stocking. You must take this gold for your dowry and demand that your father get you a husband."

In the morning the second daughter too believed that she

had had a terrible dream. And when she attempted to draw on her stocking she found in it the round bag of gold.

Then she too knew the truth and she too demanded that her father find her a husband. And she too married and went far away.

And the nobleman was as poor as ever.

Now the time came for his third and most beautiful daughter to be wed, and still he had no money for a dowry. So he said to himself, "Since I cannot in any way secure a husband for my daughter, I may as well sell her into slavery. At least I will then have enough money to comfort me in my old age."

Again he bargained with the aged woman, and again she agreed to buy the daughter.

"This time," thought the nobleman, "my daughter shall play no tricks on me. I shall sit in watch at her bedside throughout the night to see that no one visits her or brings her gifts."

So he told his daughter of a journey that they would take on the following day. And she, like the others, went to bed full of happiness. And now the nobleman sat down beside her bed to wait and to watch. He counted the hours throughout the night and at last he saw the dawn beginning to appear in the sky. "Ah, now I am safe!" he exclaimed, and promptly fell asleep.

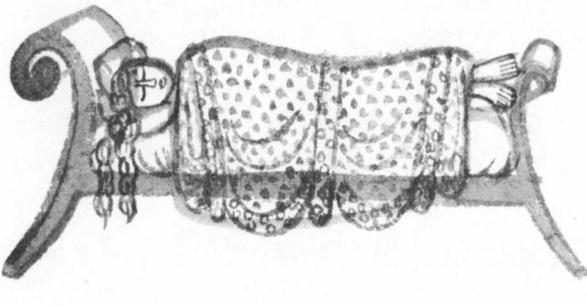

In a few moments he awakened to see a figure disappearing through the window.

"Stop thief!" he cried, "Stop thief! I will have the life of anyone who tries to rob me of my last and dearest daughter!"

He leaped through the window and pursued the stranger

through the garden and finally caught up with him at the garden wall. Then, as he drew his knife to slay the intruder, he saw that this was the young and saintly Bishop of Myra. "Oh forgive me, good Bishop," he cried. "Indeed I see how I have sinned!"

"It is not for me to forgive you," said Saint Nicolas. "Only God and your three daughters can do that." No one knows whether the three daughters ever forgave their father, but as for him, he lived from that time on a life of piety and repentance, even though he had to work for a living.

And it is because of all this that children hang up their stockings every Christmas Eve, hoping that Saint Nicolas will fill them with gifts, which of course he does.

THE PAWNBROKER AND THE GREEK

The legend of how Saint Nicolas had saved the three dowerless maidens from a life of shame spread far and wide over the country, and all the people praised the youthful bishop for the good that he had done.

Now there lived in a distant town a pawnbroker who dearly loved his many daughters. So, to honor the good Saint Nicolas and to bring good fortune upon himself and his family, he hung above the doorway of his shop three golden balls. These, he thought, would remind passers-by of the good deed of the Saint.

One day a Greek came into his shop and asked to borrow a hundred talents of gold, which he promised to return within thirty days. And seeing that the pawnbroker had hung over his door the sign of Saint Nicolas, he swore by the honor of the Saint that he would return the money.

The thirty days came and went, but the Greek did not return the money.

Then the pawnbroker called upon him to pay his debt but the Greek at first pretended that he knew of no debt, and later he said that he had paid it long ago.

So the pawnbroker went to court and the Greek was called upon to explain why he had not returned the gold.

The Greek, being wily, hid a hundred gold talents inside a long staff that he carried. He then took the staff in his hand and went to court where he stood face to face with the pawnbroker.

The Greek now pleaded that he had returned the money; the pawnbroker pleaded that he had not. The judges looked from one to another and could not decide who spoke truth, and who lied.

Then the pawnbroker said, "I will make an agreement. Let the Greek swear by the name of the good Saint Nicolas that he has returned my money. Then, if he is not struck down, I will forget my claim."

"I am willing," said the Greek, "if only you will hold my staff while I swear this oath."

So the unlucky pawnbroker held the staff wherein were hidden the hundred talents, and the Greek swore the oath, saying: "I have paid this usurer, this thief, this robber of the poor, and he has my money even now."

The pawnbroker fully expected to see the Greek struck to

the earth since he had so surely sworn to a lie. But the Greek only took back his staff and walked away, while the pawnbroker went home sorrowing that he had been betrayed by the Saint.

On the way he heard voices raised in anger. There before him he saw the Greek preparing to cross a narrow bridge. A cart was also preparing to cross the bridge and there was not room for both. "Wait!" cried the carter. "You

wait!" cried the Greek. But it happened that neither waited. The Greek was struck down by the cart; his staff was broken in two and the hundred talents of gold rolled out upon the bridge.

"You see!" cried all the people. "His trickery is exposed!" They advised the pawnbroker to pick up the talents of

gold, but he himself feared to touch the money until he should receive a sign from the Saint. But then the Greek himself rose trembling from the ground and dusted off his clothes and said to the pawnbroker, "I am the loser. Take the money, for it is yours."

And after that day all pawnbrokers in every country have hung above their doors the three golden balls of Saint Nicolas to bring good fortune upon their houses and to protect them from such scoundrels.

THE LEGEND OF A
BOY POSSESSED BY THE DEVIL

This is the story of certain events which once took place in the house of a Lycian merchant. The merchant had a son who was born on December sixth, which is the true birthday of Saint Nicolas. Because of that coincidence the merchant set aside December sixth as a day of feasting. Each year at that time he made a great banquet for all the children of his city. Rich and poor sat together on equal terms and the sons of princes ate happily beside the sons of slaves. There were lavish gifts for all the guests; for Saint Nicolas, above all other saints, is known as the saint of giving.

It came about that on a certain December sixth while the banquet was in full course and all the children were laughing and singing, a beggar came to the merchant's door asking for alms. Of course no one could know that this was no true beggar, but the Devil, who had dressed himself in rags and had come to bring some harm or disaster to those who praised Saint Nicolas.

In his generosity the merchant commanded his son to take money and gifts to the beggar in his own hands, and to invite him to sit at the head of the banquet table as their honored guest.

The boy obeyed, but after much time had passed neither he nor his guest had returned to the feast. The father went to fetch his son, but found him standing stiff and fixed as a statue.

"What ails you, my son?" he cried. "Are you not well?" The son remarked that he was perfectly well. He then went into the banquet-room, turned over all the chairs, threw the plates against the wall, and ordering all his guests to go home, he threw their gifts after them.

Then the father told his son not only to leave the room but to leave his house forever. But the boy fell to the floor as if dead, and he remained senseless for many days.

The merchant grieved, and finally set out on a pilgrimage to the city of Myra and to the church of Saint Nicolas. There he told the Saint of the terrible things that had happened in his house and asked what he could do to save his son. Saint Nicolas bade him return home and stand beside the bed where his son lay.

When the merchant was again in his house and standing beside his son's bed, Saint Nicolas, who had remained in the church, threw a beam from his own eye straight into the eye of the lifeless boy.

Then the boy opened his mouth wide and out of it stepped the Devil, who looked around and about him in fear and vanished in a cloud of smoke.

At this moment two angels passed overhead. They flew straight to the place where Saint Nicolas was and put a book in his hands. In this book were written all the signs and the marks and the gestures of the hand and the head, and all the prayers by which the Devil could be driven out of a person, once he had gotten into him. Saint Nicolas took the book under his arm, and after that he carried it with him all his life, wherever he went.

Remembering the vow that he had taken, to bring into the Church the heathen and the pagan and all worshipers of idols, and all followers of false Gods, and all those led astray by the Devil, Saint Nicolas set out once more upon his travels. Again he went on foot, taking in his hand his bishop's staff, carrying his book beneath his arm, and dressed in simple white save for the pallium about his shoulders. Thus he traveled through many countries, met with great adventures and became a martyr.

HOW SAINT NICOLAS MET AND
OVERCAME THE GODDESS DIANA

After some months of walking, Saint Nicolas came to a country where the people served idols and worshiped in the image of the false Diana. There was in this country a grove that was sacred to the goddess, and in every tree of this grove were imprisoned the spirits of the living and the dead. In one very ancient tree, it was said, the goddess herself lived. Here the people brought gifts and offerings of fish and fruit, flowers and fine cloth, and spread them out on the ground beneath the tree. Here too they made sacrifices of birds and animals or even of people to win the favor of the goddess and her help against their enemies.

Saint Nicolas came and stood beneath the sacred tree and told these people that it was wrong to shed blood or to make sacrifices. Then he preached to them about the

New Faith and told them of the Christ who had died upon a cross for the love of man.

All the people wept tears of pity and decided to leave the old faith and follow the new. Then they gathered up their gifts and cut down the sacred tree.

After that, hard times fell upon the goddess. She wandered about the country dressed in rags. Her temples were fallen to ruin and her images destroyed. She no longer lived on fine fruits and fish, but went about begging crusts from

door to door. And in her anger she decided to have
revenge upon Saint Nicolas.

So she made an oil that would burn against nature, both
in water and in rocks. Placing the oil in a vessel of gold,
she climbed to a high cliff overlooking the sea and waited.
After some days, sails appeared on the horizon, a ship
came toward her and she perceived that it was a pilgrim
ship bound for Myra.

The goddess descended from the cliff, wrapped herself in
black garments, and with a black shawl, covered the half-
moon in her hair. Taking the vessel of oil in her hand,
she set out in a small boat and went seaward to meet the
shipload of pilgrims.

The good people lifted her to the deck of the ship and
invited her to accompany them to the Church of the great
Bishop at Myra, but the goddess showed them her poverty, her ragged garments and her thin hands, and said
that she could not leave her homeland.

But she begged them to take a precious offering from her
to the Saint, saying that she had made this gift with her
own hands. Then she gave them the vessel of oil and bade

them anoint with it the feet and the robes of the Saint, and the walls of his church.

These good people promised to carry out her wish. So amid their praises and the singing of psalms, the Goddess Diana went back into her small boat and turned toward the shore.

At this time there appeared among the pilgrims a strange man who carried a staff in his hand. He asked whether he might hold in his hand the vessel of precious oil. Although they had not observed him among them before, the pilgrims trusted him and gave him the oil.

The stranger drew back his arm and threw the vessel of oil far out to sea.

The entire sea now burst into flames, against nature, and burned like a field of dry grain. The ship bearing the pilgrims, even though it was ringed by fire, suffered no damage. But the Goddess Diana was utterly consumed and was never again seen or heard of in that land. And it was in this way that Saint Nicolas banished the worship of the pagan goddess from that place.

THE THREE SCHOOLBOYS AND THE SALTING TUB

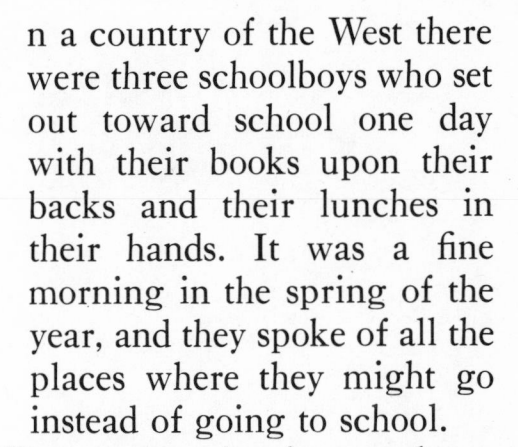 n a country of the West there were three schoolboys who set out toward school one day with their books upon their backs and their lunches in their hands. It was a fine morning in the spring of the year, and they spoke of all the places where they might go instead of going to school.

The first said, "I would like to go to the river to throw stones." The next said, "I would prefer to watch the masons who are building a tower." The third said, "I have an uncle who lives on the other side of the mountain. Let's go visit him."

The other two agreed that this idea was by far the best, so the three boys set out across the mountain with the birds singing all around them, the sun warm above them and the sky as blue as glass.

They followed first one path and then another. When they were high above the town they sat on a rock and ate their lunches. The sun shone on and they were very happy.

Still they had not reached the top of the mountain. Their path began to grow steeper, and there were more and more rocks and boulders, but the boys went on without fear. As the afternoon grew late, the sky clouded over and a

29

storm blew up and it was cold. One of the three said,
"Please, let us go back." But the other two still hoped to
reach the house of the uncle, so they persuaded the first
and they all climbed higher and higher up the mountain.
Now it became night; the wind blew stronger and the
three boys were cold and wet. They knew neither which
way to turn back nor which way to go forward. Each path

seemed more forbidding than the last and they feared to go on. So they began to search for a sheltering rock or a tree under which they could sleep until daylight.

As they wandered about on the gloomy mountain holding to each other's hands, they saw ahead of them two small lights which gleamed through the trees. The youngest boy, being fearful, whispered, "It is the eyes of some wild beast." But the other two comforted him saying, "No, no; it is the lights of a small house. Let us go and ask for shelter." As they drew nearer they saw that the lights came from an old inn that had an overhanging roof and an evil look about it. When they rapped gently they were met by a bearded man of the most ferocious appearance. But his voice was sweet, and he said to them, "Come in, dear children, you seem both wet and cold. Come sit by the fire while I make supper for you and prepare a warm bed."

They sat down and warmed and dried themselves and ate a supper of soup and good bread. Then they went to sleep in the bed that was prepared for them.

No sooner had they fallen asleep than the innkeeper, who was indeed as ferocious as his looks, crept into their room with an ax. He killed these three poor boys and cut them up and put them away to keep in a salting tub that he had for salting meat.

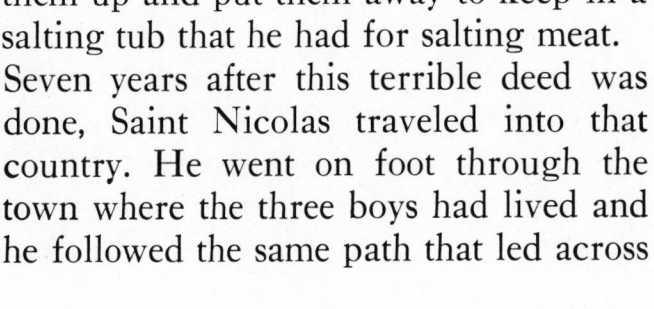

Seven years after this terrible deed was done, Saint Nicolas traveled into that country. He went on foot through the town where the three boys had lived and he followed the same path that led across the mountain. As he went upward along the path, night overtook him. Seeing the inn, he decided to stop there to eat and sleep. He too was met by the bearded innkeeper, who, when he saw that Saint Nicolas was before him, bowed low and said, "Come in, good Father, for the night is cold. I will prepare you a good meal and a warm bed." Now the innkeeper, thinking to please the Saint by serving him the finest of delicacies, took his plate and went toward the salting tub, whereupon Saint Nicolas leaped to his feet in the greatest surprise, lifted three fingers into the air and said, "Come out, dear children."

Immediately the lid of the salting tub was raised from within and the three boys stepped out hale and happy and perfectly whole. The first said, "I have slept well." The second said, "Me too." And the third said, "I dreamed I was in Paradise."

But the innkeeper was struck dumb with terror. And although some say that he repented of his evil deeds and became a good and honest man, others say that he fled through his door and was never again seen in mortal shape. Thus it was that Saint Nicolas became the patron of all schoolboys.

THE TREASURE OF BARBARUS

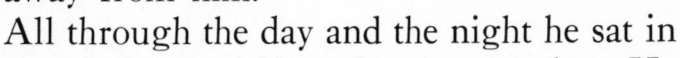

t happened that Saint Nicolas came next to a rocky island which was inhabited mainly by thieves and bandits, and he set himself to bring all these people into the Church.

There was on that island a heathen named Barbarus. This man owned a treasure of gold so vast that he dared not leave it even for an hour. He trusted neither his wife nor his sons nor his servants nor any other human being, for certainly as soon as his back was turned they would steal his gold away from him.

All through the day and the night he sat in the vault below his house where the treasure lay. He never saw the sun or the moon; he never walked in the streets or went to the houses of his friends. Even though he sometimes longed to go about like other people, he could not, for he would not leave his gold.

Barbarus had heard of the powers of Saint Nicolas and knew that he was the patron of thieves. Thus a plan occurred to him by which he might guard his treasure.

He made an image in the likeness of the Saint and he set it in the vault where the treasure was. Then he spoke to it, saying, "You, Bishop Nicolas, must watch over my treasure. If so much as one talent or a drachma or a mina is lost or stolen, I will beat you and rend you limb from limb." He then left the vault and went out to walk about in the streets.

As he walked this way and that he passed a tavern in front of which the tavernkeeper was busily sweeping the street. "Good morning," said Barbarus.

"Good morning, Excellency," said the tavernkeeper, bow-

ing low. And as soon as Barbarus had passed by, this man called six thieves that he knew and said to them, "I see that Barbarus has walked out and left his treasure unguarded."

"That's fine," said one of the thieves, "We will go and steal the gold." Another of the thieves said, "Let us, however, first drink a glass of wine to give us courage." But then a third said, "How can we drink wine when we do not have so much as a lead coin among us?"

"Well," said the tavernkeeper, "I will trust you for the wine, but you must pay me when you have the treasure." "Agreed," they all said, and drank a glass of wine.

The six thieves then went to the house of Barbarus and down into the vault, and they carried away all his treasure in bags and boxes. They took it to the inn to divide it among themselves, to drink more wine and sing songs and thus celebrate their riches.

After some time Barbarus returned to the vault, and seeing that his entire treasure had been stolen, he began to beat the image of Saint Nicolas and kick it about and hurt it cruelly. He then placed it upon a shelf, saying, "I will beat you thus and burn and rend you limb from limb each night so long as my treasure is not returned."

The six thieves sat in the tavern singing and rejoicing in their good fortune when a light appeared in the room where they were. In the center of this was the image of Saint Nicolas, now torn and battered and bleeding.

They all leaped to their feet crying out in anger, and they wrung their hands and wept tears of pity, saying, "Whoever has so beaten and abused our good Saint shall pay with his life."

"That cannot be," said the image, "for I am locked in the vault of Barbarus, who will watch over me day and night and will beat and burn and rend me limb from limb each night so long as his treasure is not returned."

The thieves then sorrowfully put the gold back into the bags and the boxes and returned it to the house of Barbarus, who was filled with wonder at the power of the image that he had made.

The six thieves now returned to the tavern to mourn their loss. But they were met there by the tavernkeeper, who said, "You have drunk my wine, now where is my money?" Since they had no money he took the shoes of one as payment, the coat of the second, the hat of the third; the fourth he made to wash his floors and dishes, the fifth to make all his beds, and the sixth to sweep the street in front of his tavern.

The rich Barbarus again sat down in the vault to guard his treasure. And although he greatly longed to walk about in the streets and see the light of day, he did not dare to leave his gold.

After many months had passed by and Barbarus had grown more and more weary, he spoke to the image, saying, "If you will but guard my treasure I will reward you in any way you wish."

The image replied, "I cannot guard your treasure, Barbarus, but I can tell you how to keep it whole and safe and undiminished for all time."

"Tell me!" cried Barbarus. "I will do whatever you command."

"First," said the image, "you must turn your gold into stones."

Even though Barbarus dreaded to do this, he obeyed, and paid out all his treasure, so that he had no more gold, but only an enormous heap of stones. Then he returned to the image to learn what he should do next.

"Now," said the image, "with these stones you must build a tower to the glory of God. And he, I pledge you, will

guard over it and protect it for all time to come."

Barbarus again obeyed and built a high domed tower which he ornamented with figures in gold and blue. He named it in honor of Saint Nicolas and placed the image that he had made above the doorway. Saint Nicolas himself came there each day, and each day he welcomed there many people of the island. So that is how the Saint, through his image, brought many heathens of this place, and even Barbarus himself, into the Church. And as he promised, the treasure of Barbarus still stands undiminished on the rocky island looking out to sea.

As for the six thieves, each one of these prospered greatly and became in time a rich and most respected man.

THE IDOL TERVAGANT

But it is told that some time later the King of Africa raided that island with his army. When he returned to his homeland he took back with him a Christian slave and the image of Saint Nicolas from above the door of the tower.

He kept the image in a closet, and from time to time he would take it out and look at it, but for the life of him he could not imagine what it was

for. At length he called the Christian slave to him and asked him the name of the image and what it could do. The slave replied that for those who had faith, the image could protect treasures, heal illnesses and predict the future. The king, thinking that the slave must be lying, said, "If what you say is true I will let you go free, but if you are lying I will cut off your head."

Now the King of Africa was an idol-worshiper. He had a golden idol named Tervagant, in which he placed the greatest trust, thanking it for his victories in war and his prosperity in peace. So he decided to test the image and the idol to see which was the more powerful and to see whether the slave lied.

On a certain night he set the idol Tervagant upon a chest full of gold; then he ordered a servant to come into the cellar and try to steal the gold. At midnight the servant came on tiptoe, set the idol on the floor and took the gold. On the following night the king set the image of Saint Nicolas upon the chest and again sent his servant into the cellar. The servant set the image on the floor and opened the lid of the chest to steal the gold. But just then the lid of the chest fell upon his neck pinning him fast

so that he had to cry for help. The Christian slave, hearing of how the servant had been trapped, now went to the king and said. "Has the image of Saint Nicolas proved true?" But the king was still in doubt. Perhaps the lid of the chest had fallen entirely by accident upon the servant's neck.

He replied, "I will make another test, and if I find that you are lying I will surely cut off your head."

At about that time the king's son fell ill and was about to die. The king, hoping to save his life, set the idol Tervagant upon a shelf above his bed, but the boy grew worse. The king now took away the idol and set the image of Saint Nicolas upon the shelf and immediately the boy began to improve and was soon well. Then the slave came again to the king and said, "Has the Saint proved true, and do you at last believe me?"

But the King of Africa could not believe that any saint could heal his son, so he decided to make a third test. "If the image fails," he said to the slave, "I will surely cut off your head."

Now he set the idol beside the image of the Saint, and he asked each one to make a prediction of the future. The idol Tervagant spoke first saying, "You will have a great gain and a great loss." But the king could not understand what was meant by these words, so he asked the idol to explain. "You will win in war," the idol said, "and that will be your gain. But you will abandon the faith of your fathers, and that will be your great loss."

When the king asked the image of Saint Nicolas to make a prediction the image said, "You will have a great loss and a great gain." The king then asked him to explain, but the image was silent and would say no more.

The king now became enraged and ordered that the Christian slave be brought to him. He raised his sword to cut off the poor slave's head, but his arm remained aloft and would no longer move, as though it had been turned to stone. He called his servants and they all tugged and pulled but they could not move his arm.

The king grew afraid and ordered his servants to release the slave and let him go free, and immediately his arm fell to his side.

At last the king was convinced that the image of Saint
Nicolas was more powerful than the idol Tervagant, so
he removed the idol from its place beside his throne
and set the image there instead. And at that moment the
idol Tervagant exploded with a loud noise and fell to the
earth in a heap of dust and ashes.

But when night came, the slave, who had once been a
robber, crept back into the throneroom of the king and
stole away the image of Saint Nicolas. He took it under
his coat and fled, and after much trouble and many adventures he at last returned to his island home and placed the
image again in its place above the door of the tower.

The king lamented this great loss, but after some time he
left the faith of his fathers and became a Christian, and
that was a great gain.

When Saint Nicolas was about to leave the rocky island, he called all the people together and spoke to them, saying, "I grieve to go away from you, my dear friends, but I shall leave in my place the image that Barbarus made in my likeness." He then charged them to look upon the image and remember the prayers and good counsels that he had given to them, and to praise God and never forget the Son who died to save all men.

Then he went upon a ship that was going to the great city of Alexandria, which was called the very fountain of all learning. There Saint Nicolas hoped to see the greatest bishops of the New Faith and to sit at their feet and learn from them. The people of the island wept to see him go, and when he had left they made many images and figures in his likeness and set them in their houses and market places, the better to remember him.

THE SEA VOYAGE
OF SAINT NICOLAS

ive days after the ship had set
sail for Alexandria, a storm
blew up and turned it out of
its course. Although the
winds died down and the
waves quieted, the sky was still
dark; the sun could not be
seen by day nor the stars by
night. Neither the helmsman
nor the sailors knew whither
they had drifted nor how to return to their course, so they
came to Saint Nicolas and begged his help.

Now the Saint took from its place at his waist a holy
cross that was made of stone and iron and wood, and he
threw this cross upon the water. At once the cross turned
and pointed so that its head was toward the north and its
longest end toward the south, and then they knew that in
that way lay the city of Alexandria.

But after five days more the ship came into a school of
fish of monstrous size and shape, and these fish plunged
and dived about her helm until they had again driven her
out of her course. And again it was many days before the
sailors could put their ship back on its way to Alexandria.
But at last they came within sight of the great city and
could see its towers rising out of the water. At this time
there surrounded the ship a sound as of voices singing,

46

and the music was as beautiful as the voices of angels.
All the sailors were charmed and fell asleep, the helmsman
fell asleep and the passengers and Saint Nicolas too. Thus
they slept and the ship took its own course and drifted for

many days and came into a strange port far past the city of Alexandria.

Now Saint Nicolas spoke to the sailors and the helmsman saying that all these things were a sign telling him not to go to Alexandria with the ship, but to go there alone and on foot. So he sent the ship on its way and stayed in that port to see what country this was and what kind of people lived there.

SAINT NICOLAS AND THE PROPHET MOHAMMED

ere the good Saint found that he had come into the domain of the Prophet Mohammed, where the people were heathens and had vowed to murder any Christian that came within their sight.

It was his wish to visit Mohammed, so he went by caravan across a desert to the citadel where the Prophet lived. There he was received with great courtesy and invited to be a guest for the evening meal.

He found the Prophet seated in a beautiful garden that was sweet with the perfume of flowers, and that echoed with the singing of birds and the sound of running brooks. In this garden was a table covered with white linen, but there was no servant in sight, nor any person who might serve a meal, nor any sign of food.

Mohammed and Saint Nicolas sat down together and immediately dishes began to appear as if by magic—bowls of soup and of rice, eggs gleaming white, and bread covered by a white napkin. But still there was no person anywhere. After this food was eaten the dishes disappeared in the same way, and other dishes came to the table—fish of many kinds, and vegetables and fresh fruit. And still not a person came into or left the garden.

49

After the meal was finished Saint Nicolas warmly thanked
the Prophet and praised the excellence of the food that
had been served. "I regret," he said, "that I am a stranger
here and have no place to which I can invite you as my
guest, for I would like to repay your kindness."
The Prophet Mohammed immediately said, "I will be
honored if you will accept as a gift from me any piece
of my lands that you will choose."
Saint Nicolas thanked him again, and he chose a piece
of earth that was dry and barren and covered with stones;
neither bush nor tree grew there, nor even weeds. There
he invited the Prophet to come as his guest on the following evening.
Mohammed wondered at so strange an invitation, but went
as he had been invited.
When he arrived at the place it was no longer barren but

had become a garden. There were trees of every sort, of fig and olive and pomegranate, some in flower and some in fruit, and there were carefully tended paths lined with the most fragrant of flowers and herbs. In the center of this garden there was an ancient vine which formed a canopy, and here was a table laid for the meal.

Saint Nicolas bowed his head to bless this meal, and after that there appeared many beautiful hands wearing rings. These hands served fine food in dishes made of gold. They then cleared away the dishes and brought bowls of water and bowls of fruit, but there was nowhere any person to be seen. After the meal was eaten, the hands played upon harps and citharas, but no players came or went.

Mohammed was greatly amazed at the wonderful things that he had seen, so on the following day he invited Saint Nicolas to walk with him.

They had not gone far when a company of men and women came toward them running. These people fell down on their knees before Mohammed and cried for help, saying that their land had become parched with heat, their crops had withered, and their wells had dried up so that there was no more water left to drink.

Mohammed led them to a place where there was a black stone. He struck the stone and immediately a stream of

water gushed out of it. The people plunged themselves into the stream, washing their hands and faces in the cool water and drinking deeply. Then they cupped their hands and tried to carry the water to their fields, but before they had gone far the water leaked out between their fingers and was lost.

Saint Nicolas reached out his hands, the palms upward toward the sky. Instantly it began to rain, and it rained for three days and three nights so that the fields grew lush with grain and flowers blossomed everywhere. The followers of Mohammed bowed low before the Saint and placed their foreheads on the earth in thanks. But Saint Nicolas asked them to stand up and to offer their thanks to God instead, and with this Mohammed agreed.

Now Mohammed searched his soul to find some new miracle to perform which would outwit the Saint and win back the awe and amazement of his people. And he decided to alarm Saint Nicolas in such a way as to make him flee from that country.

He asked the Saint to meet him at midnight in the center of a broad plain outside the city. He then ordered his servants to conceal near that place several hundreds of camels. They did so, and when Saint Nicolas arrived at the spot, they loosed the camels, whipping them and uttering loud cries. This so frightened the poor beasts that they

charged like an army across the plain, making a noise as
of thunder. Saint Nicolas stood still and was not afraid.
Then the servants of Mohammed rolled across the field
casks of oil into which they had thrust lighted torches.
Now earth and sky were lit with terrible fires as though
Hell itself had opened up and breathed its flames across
the earth, but still Saint Nicolas was not alarmed and
did not flee.

At last Mohammed clapped his hands and a host of evil
monsters appeared, leaping, snorting and uttering obscene
noises.

Thereupon Saint Nicolas struck the earth with his long
staff. A faraway rumbling began below the ground, it
came nearer and the whole plain now shook and trembled
like a leaf. Thunder roared in the skies and they turned

white with lightning, but Mohammed stood still and did not move. Saint Nicolas again struck the earth, and now it rolled and rocked and mountains were leveled to the plain; then rocks and stones were hurled out of the very heavens and Mohammed covered his head with the apron of his robe and fled. And it is said that he did not return there for twenty-five years.

After this, Saint Nicolas set out on foot across the desert.

THE MARTYRDOM OF SAINT NICOLAS

Coming at last into the great city of Alexandria, he was welcomed by the great men of the Church, by the Bishop Eusebius, by the Patriarch Alexander, by Athanasius, and by Arius the Presbyter, who became his good friend. These men told him of how, during his travels, misfortune had fallen upon the New Faith, of how many of its bishops and their followers had been imprisoned and tortured, and many more put to death. The Roman Emperor Diocletian ruled the world at that

time. He hated and feared the men of the church, despised their holiness, and commanded that wherever they were found they should be killed. And he ordered that all the people return to the worship of pagan gods and heathen idols. Since the armies and the consuls and the proconsuls of Diocletian were everywhere, only the bravest of men dared to disobey his orders.

Saint Nicolas, his friend Arius, the great Athanasius, and a few others dared to disobey. They walked about the streets of the city talking boldly to the people of the Christ who had died and of his love of man.

On a certain holiday, Saint Nicolas accompanied Arius to a great public feast that was called by the Emperor. Arriving at a wide field outside the city, they saw a scene of great magnificence. Tents, gaily striped were set about everywhere; torches, thrust into the earth on spears, filled the air with smoke and red fires; the plain was strewn with flowers trodden under the feet of throngs of people. White bulls decorated with plumes and tassels were led in and out by young girls, and boys with wreaths of leaves about their heads played on pipes and cymbals. All around were dwarfs and creatures, half-beast, half-human, that rolled

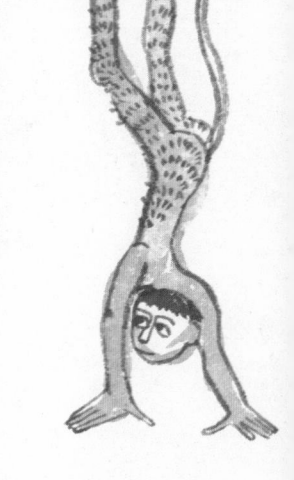

upon the ground and played strange and fanciful tricks upon the crowd.

In the center of all this there was an open place where a great ox roasted over a blazing fire. This ox, it is said, was stuffed with young lambs, and the lambs in turn were stuffed with great birds from India, which were filled with roasted capons, the capons with duck and partridge, and these with nightingales and hummingbirds. Even these smallest creatures were stuffed with clams, periwinkles and other delicacies

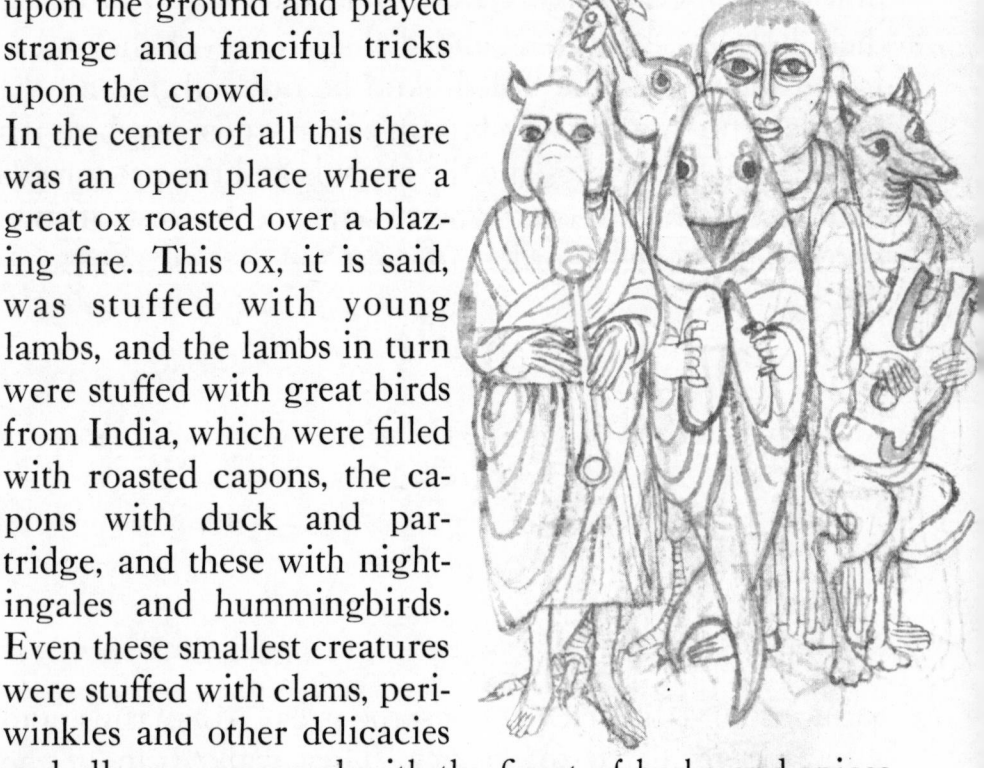

and all were seasoned with the finest of herbs and spices and garnished with fruit and flowers. Soldiers cut off the meat and passed it to the people on the tips of swords, and silver flagons filled with wine were passed about from hand to hand.

Saint Nicolas had never seen such a feast as this. He looked on in wonder as the music grew louder and faster and the shouts of the people rose like a tide.

As he watched, young men came in a procession carrying before them pagan idols of brass mounted on poles. Now Arius the Presbyter joined the procession whirling around and about in a pagan dance, mocking the name of the New Faith and ridiculing its bishops and its dead and dying martyrs.

Saint Nicolas in fury slapped his friend Arius before the great throng of people. Then he walked away from the feast. But Arius remained, and it is said in an old book that he thereafter led seven hundred virgins out of the Church and back to the worship of idols.

Now the sorrows of Saint Nicolas began. On the following day Arius called together many good men of the Church and accused Saint Nicolas, saying that he had slapped him before a public gathering, causing him great shame. The churchmen asked Saint Nicolas if this were true and he said that it was true.

So they took away from him his pastoral staff and the pallium which marked him as a bishop, and left him in dishonor.

Next Arius went to the consul of Diocletian and betrayed Saint Nicolas to him, saying that the Saint had walked about the streets of Alexandria teaching the people the New Faith. The Roman consul called Saint Nicolas before him and asked if this were true, and he said that it was true.

The consul then condemned him to be beaten and to have his flesh burned by fire, and this was done. He sent again for the Saint and asked if he would now renounce the New Faith and Saint Nicolas said that he would not.

At the consul's orders he was put into chains and thrown into a dungeon underground, where he remained alone and forgotten for a space of ten years. He received no food except bread and water. His body grew thin and his

hair white, and the clothes that he wore turned to rags on his body.

During that time the Emperor Diocletian left the throne, but Saint Nicolas remained in the dungeon, and more years went by.

Then the great Emperor Constantine came to rule the world and he was as kind as Diocletian had been cruel. He ordered that all the prisons be opened and all the poor, half-dead people inside them be set free.

Still Saint Nicolas remained in the dungeon, for he had long ago been forgotten by the bishops of Alexandria and no one else knew that he was there.

There he might have died except that on a certain night
the Emperor Constantine had a dream in which he clearly
saw a white-haired man lying on the straw of a dungeon
floor. He was curious to know who this man might be
and why he had seen him in a dream.

So he had all the prisons and the dungeons of Alexandria
searched and at last his soldiers found the Saint, who was
thin, weak and almost starved. They brought him before
the Emperor, who immediately said, "That is the man I
have seen." Then he said to Saint Nicolas, "you have

appeared to me in a dream, but I cannot tell why, nor do I know your name."

"I am Nicolas, Bishop of Myra," replied the Saint.

"If you are a bishop," said the Emperor, "where are your vestments, your pastoral staff and your pallium?"

Before the Saint could answer a radiance filled the room and there descended from Heaven two Personages who came through the windows of the palace. One carried the staff of Saint Nicolas and the other his pallium which she placed about his shoulders.

Constantine was filled with wonder and he knew that this must be a great Saint. Even though he was an Emperor he knelt and kissed the hem of the ragged garment that Saint Nicolas wore. And after that he became the first Emperor to follow the New Faith and become a Christian. In his kindness he had a ship prepared, and he sent Saint Nicolas in it with all honors back to his native land of Lycia and his church at Myra.

THE MIRACLE OF
THE MUYES OF GRAIN

hen Saint Nicolas returned to his own country he found it wasted away by famine. The fields lay dry and empty of grain, the cattle had all died and there was little left for the people to eat except such fish as could be brought in from the sea. The people, thin and ragged, all came out to greet him. And they rejoiced, for they loved him well and trusted him and believed that he could save them from their troubles.

So he embraced his friends and gave his blessing to all. Then he went to his own church to sit and try to think of some way in which he could help them.

As he sat there a messenger came to him saying that a fleet of ships had been wrecked upon the rocks of that coast and that three princes from the ships begged to speak to him.

The three princes were named Ursyn, Nepotian and Apollyn. They told him that they were cousins to the Emperor Constantine, and that they had been trusted to carry a fleet of ships laden with grain from the Emperor's granaries to the city of Alexandria. A tempest had come upon them and blown them upon the rocks. Their ships were badly damaged, they had lost many sailors, and they pleaded

that they might stay as his guests until the ships were repaired and they could sail again.

Saint Nicolas welcomed them kindly and invited them to dine with him.

But when the meal was served there was nothing to eat but one small fish.

There was no meat, there were no vegetables, there was no wine, there was not even a slice of bread. Saint Nicolas then explained that his country was in the grip of a famine. Since there was little food for the people, he himself would eat no more than they could have.

The princes praised him for his goodness but they offered him nothing of their great cargo of grain.

He then asked humbly that they spare to him one hundred muyes of grain so that he could divide it among the starving. But the Prince Ursyn, who was the oldest of the three, said, "Father, we dare not, for it is meted and measured and we must account for it even to the last handful when we reach Alexandria."

Saint Nicolas then promised that if they would but spare the grain they would find it all, even to the last handful when the ships reached the great city. But Nepotian said, "Good Father, that goes against reason."

At that time the messenger came again running and saying that four men were about to be beheaded in a place near the sea. So Saint Nicolas went immediately to the place, the princes following behind.

When they came there they found that the men about to be beheaded were sailors from the ships of Ursyn, Nepotian and Apollyn. Saint Nicolas ordered the executioner to spare the men's lives, for he said, "We allow no bloodshed here."

Prince Nepotian then replied to him, saying that the

sailors were from his ships and that if they had disobeyed it was his right to punish them by death.

"The sailors are from your ships, it is true," said Saint Nicolas, but you yourselves have begged to remain upon our soil and thus you must observe our ways and obey our will."

Then Ursyn answered, "Your country is in a state of famine, good Bishop, and you have pleaded for our help. Thus it is you who are the beggars, and we are free to do as we will."

And Nepotian said, "Now choose, Father. If you will permit us to destroy these humble and worthless sailors, we will perhaps spare to you some part of our cargo of grain."

But Saint Nicolas replied, "There shall be no shedding of blood upon this soil."

Prince Ursyn now angrily ordered the executioner to behead the four men at any cost, and the man raised his sword to obey.

But Saint Nicolas wrested the sword from his hand and threw it far out to sea so that it disappeared in the water. And the four sailors, believing that their lives were saved, clasped their hands and wept tears of joy and gratitude. At this point the Prince Ursyn and Prince Nepotian began to quarrel between themselves, for one wished to behead the Saint along with the sailors, but the other wanted to put him in chains and take him before the Emperor Constantine.

The youngest of these princes, who was Apollyn, now spoke, saying, "My dear brothers, bow down and thank this good Bishop for three times saving our lives."

When he was asked how Saint Nicolas had three times saved their lives, Apollyn replied, "First by giving us haven and refuge in our time of need; second by sparing the lives of these three wretched sailors, for we have already lost many men in the storm and without these four we could never make our way to Alexandria." But when he came to speak of the third way he was troubled and did not know.

The two older brothers were humbled and agreed to spare to Saint Nicolas the hundred muyes of grain. Then they sailed for Alexandria. When the grain was weighed and meted out to the people it was found that there was ample, both for eating and for sowing, to last two years. Yet when the grain was meas-  ured in Alexandria the holds of the ships were full and none was missing, not even so much as a handful.

Some time later these three princes were falsely accused of treason and were condemned by the Roman Consul to be beheaded. Remembering the goodness and wisdom of Saint Nicolas, they sent a messenger hurrying to him to plead for his help.

When he heard of their troubles Saint Nicolas caused the Emperor Constantine to have a dream. In this dream the Emperor saw his three cousins, the princes Ursyn, Nepotian and Apollyn walking toward him. And each of them was carrying his head upon his arm.

The Emperor wakened and hastily sent for his cousins to come before him, and thus he saved them just as they were about to die. This was the third way in which Saint Nicolas saved the lives of the three princes.

Thereafter the princes forebore to shed blood. But as for the four sailors, they told their children and their children's children of how they had been saved from death by Saint Nicolas, so that all sailors and all fishermen and all other men of the sea to this day look upon Saint Nicolas as their protector, and call on him in time of need.

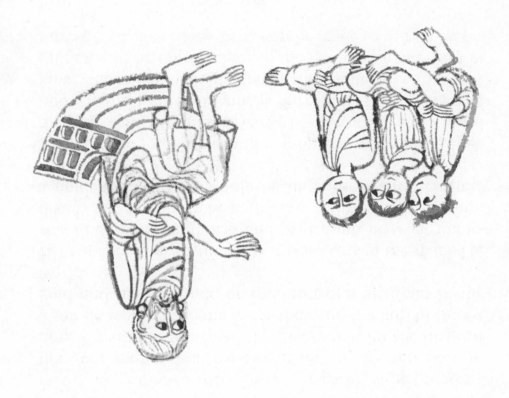

THE TWO GOLDEN CUPS

nce there was a vain man who had many daughters but no son. He wanted a son more than anything else in the world, for it seemed to him only proper that such a fine man as he should have a child who resembled him in every way.

This man kept an image of Saint Nicolas in his house, and each night he pleaded with the image, asking it to favor him with the birth of a son. Each night he promised finer and more expensive gifts if only a son were born to him. Finally he promised the image that on the birth of a son he would have made for the church a cup of purest gold and that it would be the most beautiful cup in the world.

It happened that in time a son was born to the man. He was filled with happiness and pride, and he went immediately to a famous goldsmith asking him to make for him a golden cup which would be the most beautiful in the world.

The goldsmith spent two years upon this work. He shaped the cup with the utmost care; he carved it, and chased upon it the figures of angels surrounded by leaves and vines; he set it with pearls in the shape of clusters of grapes, and he even fashioned the tendrils of the vines in purest gold. The base of the cup he made of curled leaves

of gold, and the stem he made to resemble three small
columns joined by arches, all this most skillfully wrought.
When the work was finished he brought the cup to the
vain man. They looked at it long and carefully together
and agreed that it was the most beautiful cup in the world.
In fact the cup was so very beautiful that the vain man
could not bear to give it away, so he went again to the goldsmith and asked him to make another cup as much as pos-
sible like the first, but perhaps a little smaller.

The goldsmith worked on this second cup for half a year
and then brought it to the man who thanked him and
paid him for his work.

Taking his young son with him, the vain man now set out

by ship to visit the Church of Saint Nicolas and to present the second, smaller golden cup to the Saint.

While they were at sea an enormous wave swept over the ship and carried the boy away on its crest. The sailors went out in small boats to rescue him, but they could find no trace of him anywhere and at last they came back to the father saying that the boy was drowned.

The vain man was full of grief. He tore his hair and cursed himself for his vanity, but since nothing would bring his son back to him, he decided to go on to the church and there present the cup to the Saint.

When he arrived, the church was empty, so he went straight to the altar, placed on it the golden cup that he had brought, and then prepared to leave. But as he turned, the cup fell to the floor with a loud ring. He picked it up and replaced it, but as soon as he took away his hand the cup again fell to the floor. Again he replaced it and again it fell. Now he examined the bottom of the cup, but found that it was perfectly even and flat. Nevertheless he could not make it rest on the altar without falling, so he took it away with him and returned home.

When he arrived there he went immediately to look at the first golden cup that he had made. It glittered brightly and he knew that it was surely the most beautiful one in the world. But he could no longer take the fullest pleasure in looking at it for it reminded him of his lost son and caused him to weep.

So he decided that he would at last part with this cup, and he made himself ready to go on another pilgrimage to the church of the Saint. But when he took the cup in his hands he found that he still did not want to give it away, so he put away his staff and his cloak and remained at home.

Now misfortune began to fall upon the house of this vain man. His wife and his daughters no longer loved him, but only asked him for money, and still more money, until they had spent all he had. His creditors came each day and sat in the front room of his house, and each day he had to tell them to go away, for he could not pay them. He could no longer buy the fine clothes that he liked to wear, and indeed the only comfort left to him was the great golden cup.

One day the goldsmith came to him and said a rich man would buy his golden cup and would give him enough money to pay all his creditors and allow him to live in peace.

But the vain man said, "No, I have promised the cup to another." After that he set out again for the church of Saint Nicolas, taking with him both golden cups.

When he arrived at the church he placed the smaller cup upon the altar as he had done before, and again it fell to the floor with a loud ring. Then he placed upon the altar the larger cup that was the most beautiful cup in the world, and it stayed there.

When he turned to leave he saw Saint Nicolas himself walking toward him and leading a small child by the hand, and the child was this man's son. In his great happiness and gratitude the vain man now placed the second, smaller golden cup upon the altar beside the first. And this time it remained there and did not fall.

OF A WOMAN
WHO LEFT HER BABY
TO BOIL

eople tell of a woman of Lycia who was bathing her baby one day when the Devil came along that way. The woman had already filled the tub and was about to put the child in it when she felt the water and found that it was cold. So she built a fire under the tub and as the water grew warm she set the child in it.

The Devil, who was watching through a window, now took up his flute and began to play upon it. When the woman heard the music she forgot everything that she was then doing and began to dance. Now the Devil played louder and the woman danced faster. The Devil walked away still playing and the woman danced out of door of her house, forgetting the child in the tub over the

75

fire. She danced across the garden, through the garden gate and down into the town. Wherever the Devil led, playing on his flute, the woman followed.

The townspeople all gathered to see the woman dance. They laughed and mocked and called out to her to cease her foolishness.

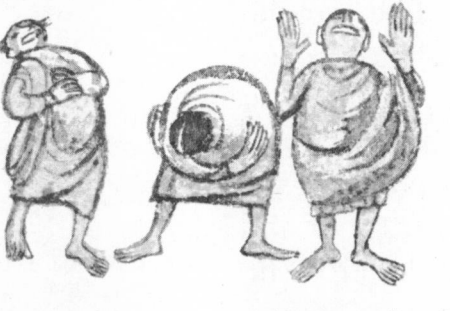

But even though she tried to stop she found that she could not. She cried out for help, but the people only laughed and no one helped her.

All day the Devil played upon his flute and all day the woman danced, and though her limbs ached with weariness she could not stop or rest.

As evening came upon them the Devil grew weary of his game, and he put away his pipe and invited the woman to sit down and rest herself, and this she did.

But as she sat down she chanced to look at the hem of his garment and saw there his cloven hoof. And then she was struck with terror, for she knew that it was the Devil who had led her away.

Then she remembered her child that she had left sitting in the bath with the fire burning underneath. And shrieking with fear and remorse, she leapt up and fled. Since they had come a long way, it took the poor woman many hours to reach her home again, and all the way she ran,

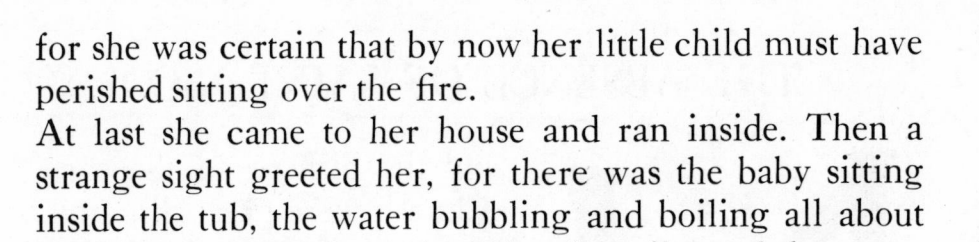

for she was certain that by now her little child must have perished sitting over the fire.

At last she came to her house and ran inside. Then a strange sight greeted her, for there was the baby sitting inside the tub, the water bubbling and boiling all about him. But he himself was laughing happily, and there was no mark nor blemish of any kind upon his skin.

The woman took the child into her arms, and wept with joy and wonder at what could have brought about this happy miracle. But as she turned she saw the good Saint Nicolas standing beside her. Then she fell on her knees to thank him. But the Saint told her to thank God instead, and he gave her forty prayers to say by which she could forever save herself from the Devil's wiles.

THE ABSENCE OF SAINT NICOLAS

Now the bishops of the early Church were great disputers, and sometimes their disputes turned into arguments, and sometimes the arguments became quarrels. When Saint Nicolas had become an old man, the disputes were so violent that the Emperor Constantine called together a congress and asked all the good men to come to an agreement with each other. And this congress was called the Council of Nicaea.

Both friends and enemies of Saint Nicolas came to Nicaea, the bishops came and the patriarchs and the Emperor himself. Arius the Presbyter, who had caused much of the quarreling, was there. And some say that Saint Nicolas was there too, while others say that he was not there.

But those who say that he was there tell of how he became weary of the arguing and fell asleep at the table in the midst of a supper. No sooner had he fallen asleep than he

78

seemed to hear voices loudly calling his name. It is said that he left his sleeping body and rose up into the air and followed the voices. He traveled for a long time through the night and a part of the day until he came to an open place in the middle of the sea where a tempest raged. The wind lashed about him, the sky was white with lightning and the waves rose up like mountains.

In the center of all this turbulence Saint Nicolas saw a ship in great distress, its masts broken and its sails torn away. On the ship there were sailors who clung to the masts and cried pitifully for his help.

So he lifted his hands and calmed the waves, and caused the thunder and lightning to cease, and then he brushed the rolling clouds out of the sky, so that the sun shone and the sea was calm. The sailors cried out their gratitude

and said many prayers of thanks. Saint Nicolas blessed
them and turned back to Nicaea, where he awakened at
the table rubbing his eyes.

Some time had passed while he was away and the Council was now ended. The wicked Arius had been condemned as an enemy to the Church, the troubles and the arguments were settled and all the bishops and other holy men were preparing to leave. They now gathered around Nicolas and said, "Brother, we have missed you, for many things have happened while you slept."

Saint Nicolas replied, "Indeed yes, a ship has been rescued from sinking and many good mariners have been saved." The Fathers thought that he meant to say that the Church was a ship and that its souls were like mariners upon the sea. Thus they all agreed and praised him for his wisdom and departed.

So those who say that Saint Nicolas was at the Council of Nicaea are right and those who say that he was not there are right, for he was both there and not there.

DEODONE

nce there was a man named Getro and he had a son named Deodone, which means "God Gave." He named his son this way because he thought that any child so beautiful as this one must have been sent by God himself. Getro had one great fear. It was that the Saracens might some day steal away his son. For these fierce people often raided his country, and when they did they took away sheep, money and clothing. And sometimes they stole people too, especially children.

Hoping to gain the protection of Saint Nicolas for his son, Getro built a beautiful chapel in his honor. Then he took the boy with him and made a pilgrimage to the city of Myra to see the Saint and plead for his help. Saint Nicolas received Getro and Deodone and listened to their plea. He told them to have no fears and promised that he would watch over the boy, and that he would keep him safe from all pain and harm and suffering.

After that time the father and the son always marked the birthday of Saint Nicolas with great feasting and joy. But it happened that on such a day the Saracens raided that country and took away many captives, among them Deodone.

When the Saracens returned to their own country they reported to their king that they had taken much plunder and had brought him many slaves. He looked at them all, and when he saw Deodone he loved him dearly and said that he would keep him as his own slave.

But he treated Deodone more as a son than as a slave. He dressed him in fine clothes and gave him every gift that he thought might please a boy. Each day he asked Deodone what thing would please him most, and each day Deodone replied, "I want only to return to the house of my father, Getro." And that was the only kindness that the king refused him. Indeed, he wept whenever he thought that he might lose the boy.

Deodone suffered neither pain nor harm, and the king pleaded with him to be happy and willing to remain among the Saracens, but Deodone only longed to return home. Then the king offered to make him heir to all his lands and promised that he would rule his people, and still Deodone refused.

After a number of years had passed, it happened that on a feast day of Saint Nicolas, Deodone chanced to think of his home and his father and his mother, and of all the people who would be laughing and singing to celebrate the Saint's Day. Then he began to weep bitterly.

The King of the Saracens called him to his throne and asked what caused him to cry. And Deodone replied, as always, "I long to return to the house of my father."

The king now began to grow angry. He asked Deodone to bring him a cup of wine and the boy did so, but in his unhappiness he shed tears into the wine. At this the king became suddenly enraged. All his kindness was now gone, and he ordered a whip and began to beat the boy violently so that he bled and suffered terrible pain.

Now Saint Nicolas, far away, heard the boy's cries. And

remembering his promise to keep him from all pain and suffering, he went through the air to the palace of the King of the Saracens. Then, lifting Deodone gently by the hair of his head, he flew away with him over cities and rivers and mountains until he reached his home, and there he set him down before the chapel and the house of his father.

Getro was full of gratitude and it is said that he set out again with his wife and his son to visit the church of Saint Nicolas, to bring him gifts and to thank him. But on arriving at the church he found the good Saint lying dead upon his bier.

Getro and his wife and his son fell down upon their knees and wept in sorrow. And as they knelt there they saw seven angels come into the church and carry away the soul of Saint Nicolas.

THE MIRACULOUS MANNA
OF SAINT NICOLAS

he body of Saint Nicolas was buried in a casket beneath the floor of his church in Myra, and there it remained for exactly seven hundred and forty-four years. Armies overran the land and were beaten back; kings came and went, and some died quietly and others were murdered, but Saint Nicolas slept on in peace.

At last the enemy Seljuks took the country and kept it. As they held the church in contempt, they allowed no one to come there to pray or sit or pay homage to the Saint. The church fell into ruin; weeds grew out of the roof and walls, and dust and rubble slowly filled the inner chambers. Then, on a dark night, a small band of sailors came into the country by stealth and they dug up the body of Saint Nicolas and carried it away to Bari in Italy. The  people of that town praised the sailors for their daring. Then they built a new church and re-buried the casket. No sooner was this done than a miraculous fluid, golden, of the color of honey, began to issue from the tomb. This fluid, it was said, would cure the lame and the blind and thus it was called "the Miraculous Manna of Saint Nicolas." From that time on, even to the present day, people have come there from all parts of the earth, some to be cured, others only to give praise to the good Saint.

So ends the story of the great Saint Nicolas, called the Thaumaturge, or, "one who makes miracles."